Roar... I am a lion.
I like to relax after a hot day
on the savanna!

Snap... I am a crocodile.
I open my great, big jaws
to catch food!

Miaow... I am a cat.
I love to explore the streets
and countryside!

Woof... I am a dog.
I wag my tail and play with
my ball in the backyard!

Tweet... I am a bird.
I like to catch up with my friends on the telephone line!

Chatter... I am a monkey.
I like playing in the treetops
high above the ground!

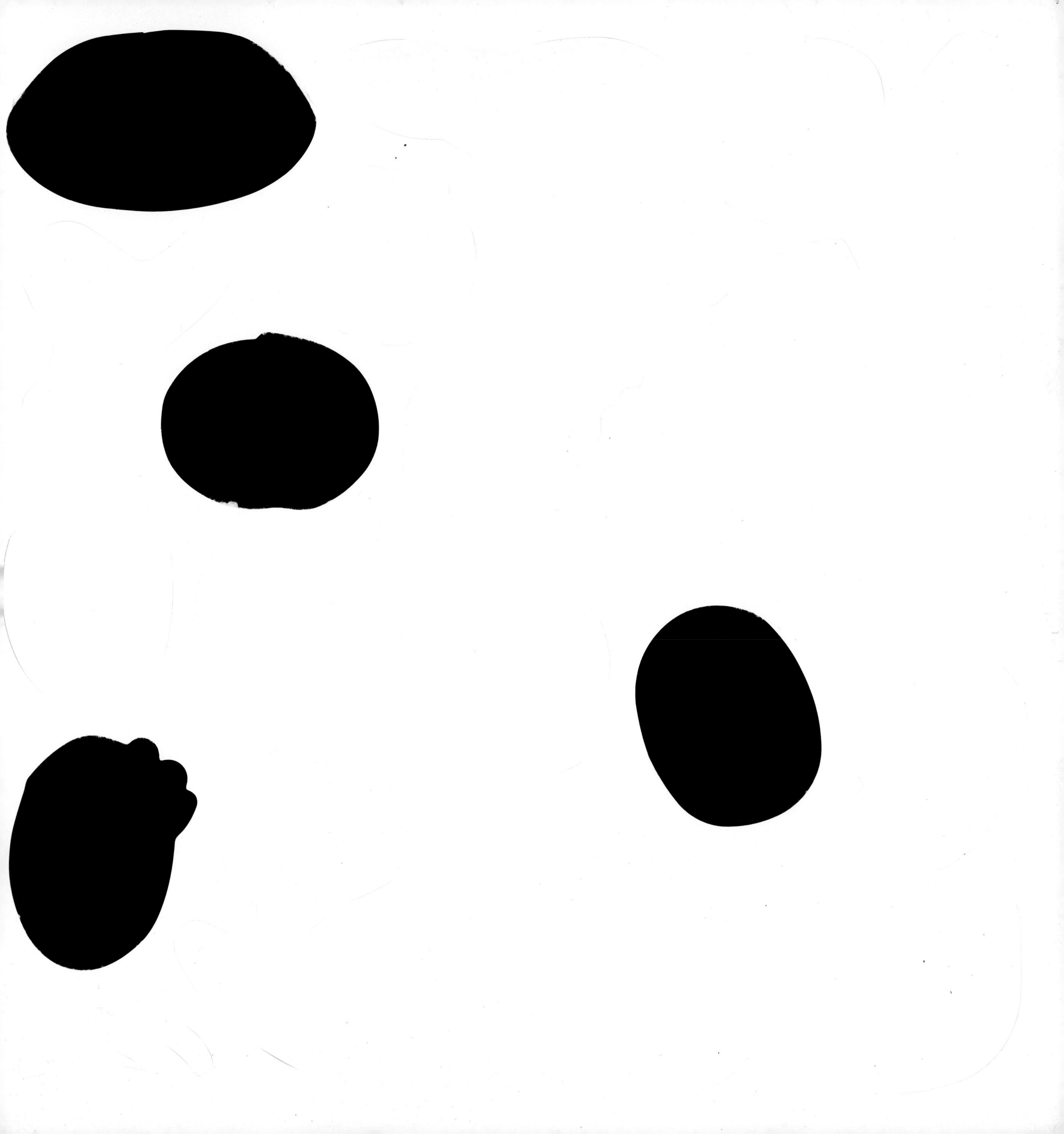

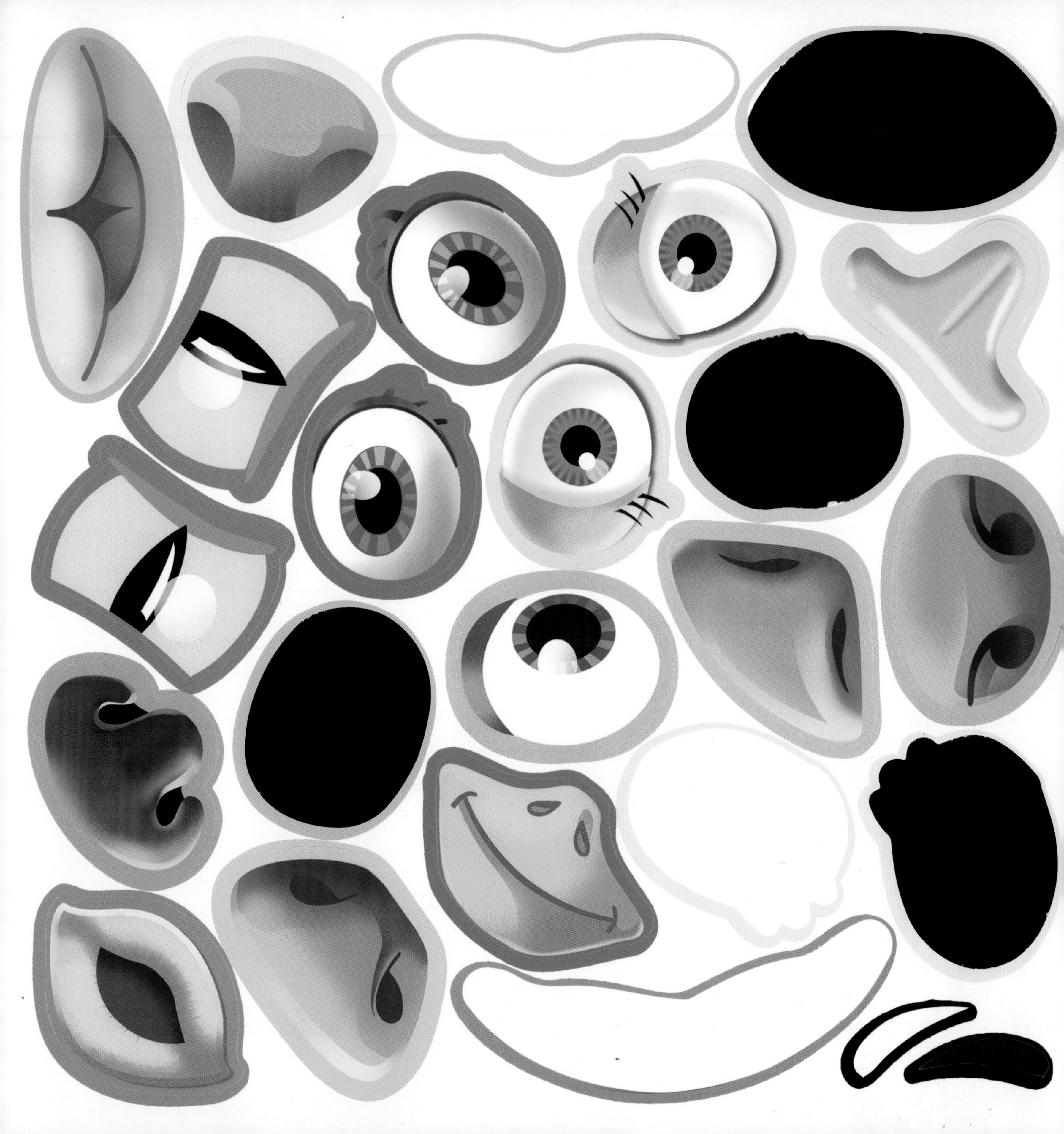

Plod... I am a camel.
I can walk for long distances under
the hot desert sun!

Neigh... I am a horse.
I love to gallop fast around
my paddock!

Gulp... I am a fish.
I like to swim through the bubbles
in my fish tank!

Sniff... I am a rabbit.
I love to hop around in my field and
crunch on juicy carrots!